THE
MAGIC LAKE

"A MYSTICAL, HEALING LAKE OF THE CHEROKEE"

By Tom B. Underwood
Illustrations By Shirley Simmons

Somewhere in the mist-covered peaks of the Great Smoking Mountains, Cherokee legends from Ancient times told of a magic lake that could heal the wounds and sores of all living things.

Here to this lake the wild things could come to wash away the gashes of an arrow or the wounds of a fall.

All Cherokee children heard the story of the magic Lake.

Nobody knew where it was except maybe a Medicine Man.

Near the head of the mighty river in the land of the Smoking
Mountains lived a Great Hunter, called Walk The Forest. Walk The
Forest was a Cherokee Indian whose brothers were known as the people
of the Deer Clan. He grew up in the wildest, most rugged part of the
Smoking Mountains, where he learned the art of hunting from a great
Chief called Running Deer.

Chief Running Deer taught Walk The Forest how to use his blow-gun for small birds and his bow for big game like bear and deer. When Walk The Forest had learned how to use these weapons the Chief showed him how to trail wounded animals through the woods by watching to see how the leaves and grass were bent or broken. Chief Running Deer taught him to keep trailing wounded animals until he found them no matter how long it took. After the young hunter had learned how to do all these things he would go into the forest for weeks at a time to hunt. Many cold winter days he spent on the trail of deer and bears. He would always hunt until he could come home with something to eat for his family.

Walk The Forest grew up to be tall and strong like the great chiefs of his people. His eyes were sharp and he could see anything that moved in the dim forests. He could smell the scents of the bear and deer and knew where their trails were. He could run for hours at a time without rest. Walk The Forest hunted the big black bears that lived among the hemlocks on the high, high ridges. There was one great bear that Walk The Forest had tried to kill many, many times. This great black bear was wise to the ways of the Indian hunters and always disappeared when someone tried to kill him. One day the mighty hunter said "I will go into the forest and kill the great black bear. I shall never return until I have slain him."

So Walk The Forest went into the woods and searched for many days. He traveled along cool mountain streams. He saw squirrels and chipmunks scamper in the leaves in search of food. Finally after a long time the hunter found the track of the Great Bear. He tried in many ways to get near enough to the bear to shoot him with his hunting arrow. Then one day after he had been trailing the bear all day he came over a small hill where he saw him eating berries in a thicket. Walk The Forest quickly lay down on his stomach and began to crawl to a large tree that was between him and the Great Bear. When he reached the tree the mighty hunter stood up and drew his bow until the long hunting arrow was all the way back. He took careful aim at the Great Bear and let the arrow go. It flew straight at the bear and hit him in the side. The bear gave a loud scream and lunged into the woods.

It was late in the afternoon when Walk The Forest shot the bear so he said to himself, "I will let the spirit of the Great Bear die before I go find him. I will sleep here in the forest until the sun rises again, so that I may follow the trail of the bear to where his spirit has died."

That night Walk The Forest made a shallow hollow in the ground and filled it with the green twigs of the hemlock tree. This was his bed in the forest. He built a small fire and roasted deer meat from his hunting pouch. Then he lay down on his bed of hemlock twigs and slept.

When the full light of day came, Walk The Forest rose from his bed and started again to follow the trail of the bear. Through hemlock trees and over rock gorges, through laurel thickets and swampy springholes the trail of the bear wandered. The spirit of the bear did not die as Walk The Forest had thought. All day the hunter tracked the Great Bear. Sometimes he would have to double back to be sure he had not lost the trail. At other times the trail would be as new as if the bear had rested a while before he moved on.

Once Walk The Forest found where the bear had lain down and left small patches of blood. When he found this place he knew that the bear was very near. Finally, near the end of the second day, the trail of the bear started up the biggest of the Smoking Mountains. The track led up, up the side of the high mountain. Walk The Forest followed the track until the sun again hid itself behind the far away ridges.

That night the hunter found a small cave under a huge rock where he made his bed of soft mountain ferns. He built a little fire to warm himself by. His hunting pouch was empty of food so he gathered the younger limbs of the birch tree to chew so that his strength would not fail him. As he lay down to sleep in the cold high air he heard the distant howl of the timber wolf. Walk The Forest hoped that the wolf was not calling his mates to help him kill the great bear. Then the tired hunter fell asleep.

68

Three more days the weary hunter followed the
trail of the wounded bear. Sometimes he was very
near the bear, but not near enough to kill him. When
he was almost to the top of the tallest mountain he
grew so weary he was barely able to walk. At last he
crawled across the top of the mountain and saw before
him a large field that was covered with long green
grass. The Great Bear he had been trailing so long was
lying asleep at the edge of the field.

SHIRLEY
69

Just when the weary hunter saw the bear he too fell fast asleep. In a very short time he awoke to see before him a beautiful lake from which a gray mist was ever rising. In the edge of the water the Great Bear was swimming and bathing himself. The big jagged hole in his side had healed and the Great Bear was well again. Walk The Forest gazed in trembling wonder at the shimmering mystic lake. As he gazed he saw other animals swimming and bathing in the mysterious waters. As Walk The Forest watched he remembered all the stories of the Cherokee storytellers. He remembered what they had said about the magic lake. Many of the old Cherokee people had heard how the magic lake healed the wounded animals and gave them new spirits but no one had ever seen it or knew where it was.

As the hunter watched the animals playing in the shimmering light of the lake a huge black cloud began to roll over the mountains. Out of the heavens came a thundering cloud of wind and rain. The lightning flashed as the hunter sat shaking with fear. All around him was darkness. Then a loud angry voice spoke from the darkness and said, "Go, mighty hunter to the council of your people and tell them they must not follow the wounded animals to the lake of the mists. If your people disobey the Great Spirit, the magic lake will dry up and your bear and deer will vanish forever."

Trembling with fear, Walk The Forest rose and looked again for the Great Bear but he had disappeared and instead of the magic lake the field of long green grass glistened in the emerging sunlight. Walk The Forest sat there and thought a long time at the edge of that green field high in the Smoking Mountains. It was hard for him to believe that the wind and rain and mighty voice had come out of the sky, but he could feel the wet raindrops on his body and could see the glistening field.

Then the mighty hunter thought to himself. "The Great Spirit has spoken to the mighty hunter and I must obey him. I must go to my people and warn them."

Down off the mountain so high the mighty hunter came. It was a long, long way to where his village was by the great river, but Walk The Forest traveled almost without rest. He was anxious to see his people and tell them what had happened to him. He traveled by day and night until he came to the place of the high rocks. There he was forced to rest for fear that in the night he would fall into the deep river below.

The next day the mighty hunter walked into his village. The people were all very happy to see their brother, the mighty hunter. They gathered around him asking where he had been so many suns and what had he done. Then they all began to say, "Where is the Great Bear that Walk The Forest has sworn to kill? Has our great hunter failed to kill the big bear?"

Walk The Forest held up his hand and said, "Many days and nights I have been away from my people. I found and shot the Great Bear with my hunting arrow. Across the far places of our big mountains I trailed the wounded bear. Then finally I trailed him up the highest of all the mountains where I found him at the Magic Lake. When I last saw the Great Bear he was healed of his wound from my hunting arrow. The mystic waters had made him well again. But as I gazed in wonder at the magic waters, the Great Spirit spoke to me from a thundering cloud of wind and rain. He told me to tell my people that they must not follow the wounded animals to the Magic Lake. He said, "If the people do not obey him he will cause the lake to dry up so that the animals will die and our game will vanish forever."

Today this great smoking mountain has a field of glistening grass but no one has seen the Magic Lake since Walk The Forest came back from hunting the Great Bear.